COUNTRY
THE TOP 100 OF 1981

From Columbia Pictures Publications

©1981
Columbia Pictures Publications
16333 N.W. 54th Ave., Hialeah, Florida 33014

ISBN No. 0-89898-103-4

COUNTRY
THE TOP 100 OF 1981

Art: Shirley Butzer / Editor: Carol Cuellar / Production: Frank J. Hackinson / Printer: Central Litho (Miami)

THE HOUSE OF THE RISING SUN

Arrangement by
DOLLY PARTON and
MIKE POST

There is____ a house____ in New____ Or - leans,____

____ down in the Vieux Car - re';_____

2.3. they call the Ris - ing Sun;_____

The House Of The Rising Sun - 4 - 1

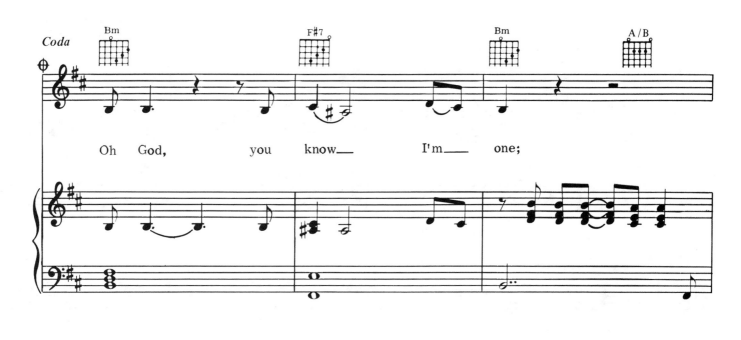

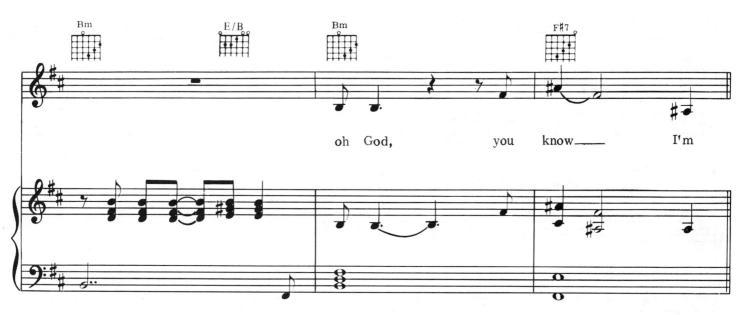

FANCY FREE

Words and Music by
JIMBEAU HINSON and
ROY AUGUST

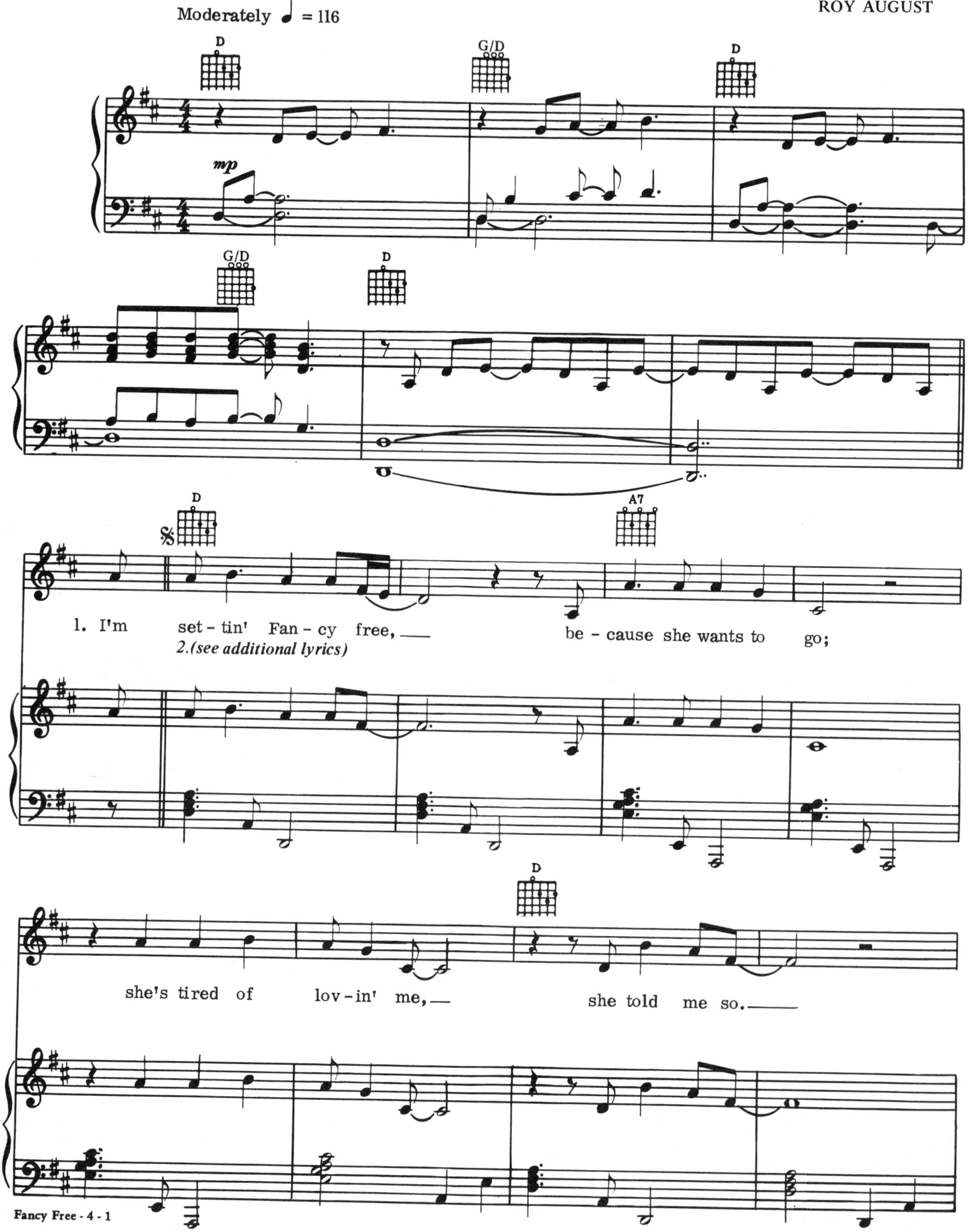

Moderately ♩ = 116

1. I'm set-tin' Fan-cy free, ___ be-cause she wants to go;

2. (see additional lyrics)

she's tired of lov-in' me, ___ she told me so. ___

Fancy Free - 4 - 1

I guess she don't know____ just how much____ she means to me, ____ but a - long with all____ my dreams, I'm set - tin' Fan - cy free. ____

Yes, I'm set - tin' Fan - cy free, ____ e - ven though____ I love her still; ____ she'd

Chorus:

mf

Fancy Free - 4 - 2

10

Verse 2:
Oh Lord, you just don't know how it hurts to say good-bye;
She did her best to stay; I can't say she did not try.
I just hope the road she takes leads back to me;
So along with all my dreams, I'm settin' **Fancy free.**
(To Chorus:)

I WOULDN'T HAVE MISSED IT
FOR THE WORLD

Words and Music by
KYE FLEMING, DENNIS MORGAN
and CHARLES QUILLEN

Moderately Fast

1. Our paths may nev-er cross_ a-gain;_
2. (see additional lyrics)

may-be my heart_ will nev-er mend,_

but I'm glad for all the good_ times. You brought me so_

I Wouldn't Have Missed It For The World - 3 - 1

Verse 2:
They say that all good things must end.
Love comes and goes just like the wind.
You've got your dreams to follow,
But if I had the chance tomorrow,
You know I'd do it all again.
(To Chorus:)

From the Twentieth Century-Fox film "9 to 5"

NINE TO FIVE

Words and Music by
DOLLY PARTON

Lively 𝅗𝅥 = 104
mf
mf
G
C
Tum - ble out of bed and stum-ble to the kitch - en; pour my - self a cup
2. (see additional lyrics)
G
D
of am - bi - tion, and yawn, and stretch, and try to come to life.
G
Jump in the show - er, and the blood starts pump - ing;

Verse 2:
They let you dream just to watch them shatter;
You're just a step on the boss man's ladder,
But you've got dreams he'll never take away.
In the same boat with a lot of your friends;
Waitin' for the day your ship'll come in,
And the tide's gonna turn, and it's all gonna roll your way.
(To Chorus:)

Chorus 4 , 6:
Nine to five, they've got you where they want you;
There's a better life, and you dream about it, don't you?
It's a rich man's game, no matter what they call it;
And you spend your life putting money in his pocket.

STEP BY STEP

Words and Music by
EDDIE RABBITT, EVEN STEVENS
and DAVID MALLOY

1. She seems a mil - lion miles a - way.
2. *(see additional lyrics)*

When she walks by you don't know what to say.

You're gon - na make your move; you bet - ter make it now.

Step By Step - 4 - 1

Step By Step - 4 - 2

Verse 2:
She looks too beautiful to touch,
But your heart keeps talking to you;
Now, don't give up.
You think you see something in her eyes,
But you will never know until you try.
But you've got to take that....
(Chorus)

Step By Step - 4 - 4

TIGHT FITTIN' JEANS

Words and Music by
MIKE HUFFMAN

Tight Fittin' Jeans - 3 - 1

and she knew I saw right through her tight fit - tin' jeans.

2. I jeans.

1. She said I mar-ried mon-ey; I'm used to wear-ing
2. Well, now she's back in her world, and I'm still stuck in

pearls, but I've al-ways dreamed of be-ing just a good ol' boy's girl;
mine; but I know she'll al-ways re-mem-ber the time

so to-night I left those crys-tal can-dle lights to live a dream, and
a cow-boy once had a mil-lion-aire's dream, and

24

Verse 2:
I asked her what's a woman like you doing here?
I see you're used to champagne, but I'll buy you a beer;
She said you've got me figured out, but I'm not what I seem;
And for a dance I'll tell you about these tight fittin' jeans.

Verse 3:
We danced every dance and Lord, the beer that we went through;
I'm satisfied I did my best to make her dream come true.
As she played out her fantasy before my eyes, it seemed
A cowgirl came alive inside those tight fittin' jeans.

Verse 4:
In my mind she's still a lady; that's all I'm going to say,
But I knew that I'd been broken, by the time we parted ways;
And I know I held more woman than most eyes had ever seen,
That night I knew a lady wearing tight fittin' jeans.

Tight Fittin' Jeans - 3 - 3

WHAT'S NEW WITH YOU

Words and Music by
DEAN DILLON and
CHARLES QUILLEN

1. Well, hel - lo; how have you been?
2. *(see additional lyrics)*

You're a sight to see;— yes, I've still got that old

job down at the fac - to - ry. Well,—

What's New With You - 3 - 1

Verse 2:
Well, the years haven't changed you;
You're still looking good.
No, the years haven't changed me,
The way I hoped they would;
And it looks like looking back is all
That I look forward to;
(Spoken:) But tell me honey,
(Sung:) What's new with you? *(To Chorus:)*

Bridge 3:
And it looks like looking back is all
That I look forward to;
(Spoken:) But tell me honey,
(Sung:) What's new with you?

Columbia Pictures Presents Neil Simon's "ONLY WHEN I LAUGH"

ONLY WHEN I LAUGH

Words by RICHARD MALTBY, Jr.

Music by DAVID SHIRE

30

Only When I Laugh - 5 - 3

31

Only When I Laugh - 5 - 4

YOU
(Make Me Wonder Why)

Words and Music by
RAFE VANHOY and
DEBORAH ALLEN

Moderately Bright ♩ = 138

You(Make Me Wonder Why) - 3 - 1

You (Make Me Wonder Why) - 3 - 2

CRYING IN THE RAIN

Words and Music by
CAROLE KING and
HOWARD GREENFIELD

Crying In The Rain - 2 - 1

(There's) NO GETTIN' OVER ME

Words and Music by
TOM BRASFIELD and
WALT ALDRIDGE

1. Well, you can walk out on me to - night,___ if you
2. say that you need to be free,___ but there ain't

think that it ain't feel-in' right,___ but dar - ling,
no place that I won't___ be;___ sweet dar - ling,
there ain't

no get - tin' o - ver me.___

(end solo)

2. Well, you can

(There's) No Gettin' Over Me - 3 - 1

THE PLEASURE'S ALL MINE

Words and Music by
CURLY PUTMAN and
KIERAN KANE

42

Chorus:

mine, _____ when you're sat - is -

fied; _____

ooh _____ ba - by, _____ the pleas - ure's all

mine. 2.And

The pleas - ure's all

BY NOW

Words and Music by
CHARLES QUILLEN, DON PFRIMMER
and DEAN DILLON

Slowly and tenderly

1. By now she's put-ting on her make up;
2. By now she knows how much she needs me

bet she's been cry-in' all night long.
'cause she can't make it on her own.

3. (see additional lyrics)

By Now - 3 - 1

Verse 3:
By now she's slipped into her nightgown,
And she's letting down her soft brown hair.
By now she needs someone to hold her,
And I know she's wishing I was there.

ALL ROADS LEAD TO YOU

Words and Music by
KYE FLEMING and
DENNIS MORGAN

1. Black-top's burn-ing, heat waves__ rise,__ pick up my shov-el, put my
2. (See additional lyrics)

back to the grind;__ got an-oth-er job in Flag-staff when this one's

paved.

I work the free-way, the pay's all__ right,__

All Roads Lead To You - 3 - 1

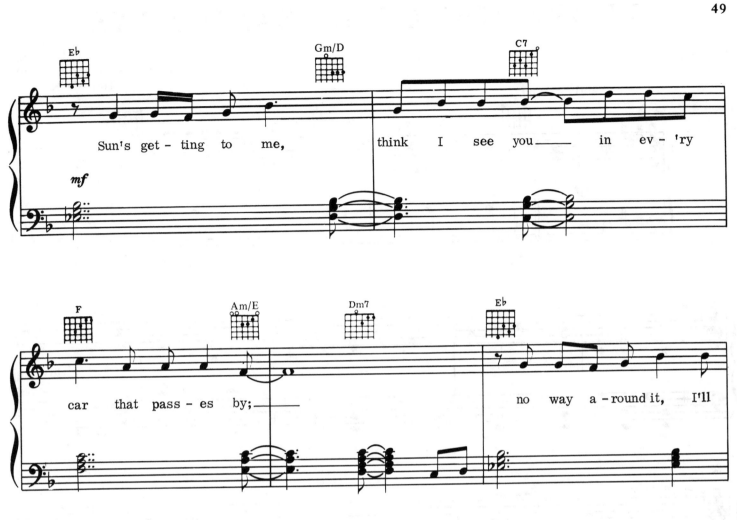

Sun's get-ting to me, think I see you___ in ev-'ry car that pass-es by;___ no way a-round it, I'll

al-ways love you; an-y fool___ can read the signs.

D.S.S.

Verse 2:
The boss says one more mile to go,
The last one always goes so slow.
If I could just turn off my mind I'd be all right;
But I keep wondering what went wrong,
Who's holding you now that I'm gone;
There's not a minute that goes by you don't cross my mind.
(To Chorus:)

All Roads Lead To You - 3 - 3

I LOVE YOU A THOUSAND WAYS

Words and Music by
LEFTY FRIZZELL and
JIM BECK

you, I'll prove it in days to come;_____ I swear it's
2. true, I'll prove it to you some day;_____ I love
3.(see additional lyrics)

true, dar - ling, you're the on - ly one;_____ I think of
you, in my heart you'll al - ways stay;_____ I've been so

you, of the past and all our fun;_____ I love
blue, and lone - some ev - 'ry day;_____ I love

I Love You A Thousand Ways - 2 - 1

Verse 3:
So darling, please wait, please wait and you will see;
There'll be a change, a great change made in me;
I'll be true, you never will see blue days;
I love you ... *(To Coda)*

NOBODY'S FOOL

Words and Music by
DON COOK, RAFE VANHOY and
DEBORAH ALLEN

Nobody's Fool - 3 - 1

Nobody's Fool - 3 - 2

54

Verse 2:
I pull out my excuses, and tell them to the wall;
My alibis are useless in the silence of it all.
It's harder being wrong than it ever was before,
Nobody's fool, nobody's fool, nobody's fool anymore.

Verse 3:
Can't believe I miss you, why does it hurt me so;
To be the last to fall in love, and the only one to know?
Too late I see too clearly what a fool I was before;
Now I'm nobody's fool, nobody's fool, nobody's fool anymore.

Nobody's Fool - 3 - 3

LONGING FOR THE HIGH

Words and Music by
O.B. McCLINTON and
STEVE McCORVEY

Longing For The High - 3 - 1

side of a bed.___ When you don't have to touch___ 'em to get a thrill,___you'll know the

love in your heart___ has got to be real._____

And then she said;

1. real.

2. Yes, I'm real._____

3. Yes, I'm real. Can't___ you see I'm

YOUR GOOD GIRL'S GONNA GO BAD

Words and Music by
GLENN SUTTON and
BILLY SHERRILL

I've nev-er seen__ the in-side of a bar-room_____ Or lis-tened to__ a juke box all night long,_____ But I see these are__ the things that bring you pleas-ure,_____ So I'm gon-na make some chang-es in our home.__

Your Good Girl's Gonna Go Bad - 3 - 1

I've heard it said,___ if you can't beat 'em, join 'em,___
ev - en learned___ to like the taste of whis - key;___

So if that's the way___ you've want-ed me___ to be,___ I'll
In fact you'll hard - ly rec-og - nize___ your wife.___ I'll

change if it ___ takes that___ to make you hap - py.___ From now
buy some brand ___ new clothes___ and dress up fan - cy.___ For my

on you're gon - na see___ a diff-'rent me,___ Be - cause your
jour - ney to___ the wild - er side of life.___ Oh, yeah, your

Your Good Girl's Gonna Go Bad - 3 - 2

60

Your Good Girl's Gonna Go Bad - 3 - 3

PRIDE

Words and Music by
WAYNE P. WALKER and
IRENE STANTON

Pride - 3 - 1

me look like a cra - zy___ fool,___ so why___
heart - aches are what you will put me___ through,___

___ do I have these doubts a - bout leav - ing

you?___ My heart tells me stay but my

pride tells me go; how can I leave you when

I love you so?_____ Which way shall I

turn? I'd sure like to know; my

heart tells me stay, but my pride_____ tells me

go._____ I'd

I'LL LEAVE THIS WORLD LOVING YOU

Words and Music by
WAYNE KEMP

I'll leave_____ this world lov-ing you. Walk a-

way, ba-by, leave with my bless-ings;_____ once in a-
take ev-'ry-thing but my mem-'ries,- for they're__

while,_____ let me hear from you. If we
good__ ones, and they'll see me through. If we

nev-er meet a-gain be-fore_____ my_____ life is o-ver,
nev-er meet a-gain this side of I'll love you for-ev-er,
nev-er meet a-gain this side of heav-en,_____ I'll

I'll Leave This World Loving You - 2 - 1

JUST ENOUGH LOVE
(For One Woman)

Words and Music by
DANNY MORRISON and
DAVE KIRBY

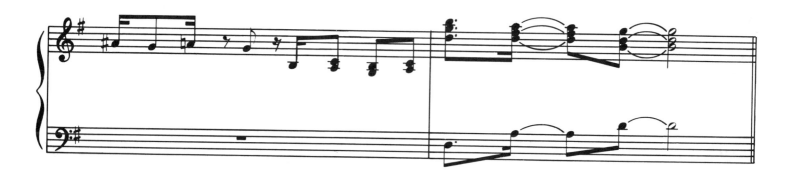

Just Enough Love (For One Woman) - 2 - 1

Just Enough Love (For One Woman) - 2 - 2

I WANT YOU TONIGHT

Words and Music by
STEVE DAVIS

I Want You Tonight - 2 - 1

Verse 2:
But if that girl over there would look my way,
I'd take her in my arms, this is what I'd say,
"I'm tired of messin' around girl; I want you tonight."
(To Chorus:)

Verse 3:
The touch of silk, a trace of perfume;
She danced on flames burning in the room;
She walked up next to me, smiled, and ordered chablis.

Verse 4:
We started talkin, I bought her a drink;
She came on so warm, I didn't have to think;
She looked into my eyes, you'll never guess what she said.
(To Chorus:)

Chorus 2:
She said I want you tonight;
She said I want you tonight;
I'll take a chance and give my heart to you;
We'll never know 'til we try.
She said I want you tonight;
She said I want you tonight;
I can't promise it will last forever,
I just want you tonight.
(To Coda:)

MONA LISA

Music and Words by
JAY LIVINGSTON and
RAY EVANS

Mo - na Li - sa, Mo - na Li - sa, men have named you. You're so

like the la - dy with the mys - tic smile. Is it on - ly 'cause you're lone - ly__ they have

blamed you for that Mo - na Li - sa strange-ness__ in your smile? Do you

Mona Lisa - 2 - 1

smile to tempt a lov-er,— Mo - na Li - sa, —— or is this your way to hide a bro - ken

heart? Man - y dreams have been brought to your door - step. They just lie there, and they

die there. Are you warm, are you real, Mo - na Li - sa, or just a

cold and lone - ly, love - ly work of art? Mo - na art?

PARTY TIME

Words and Music by
BRUCE CHANNEL

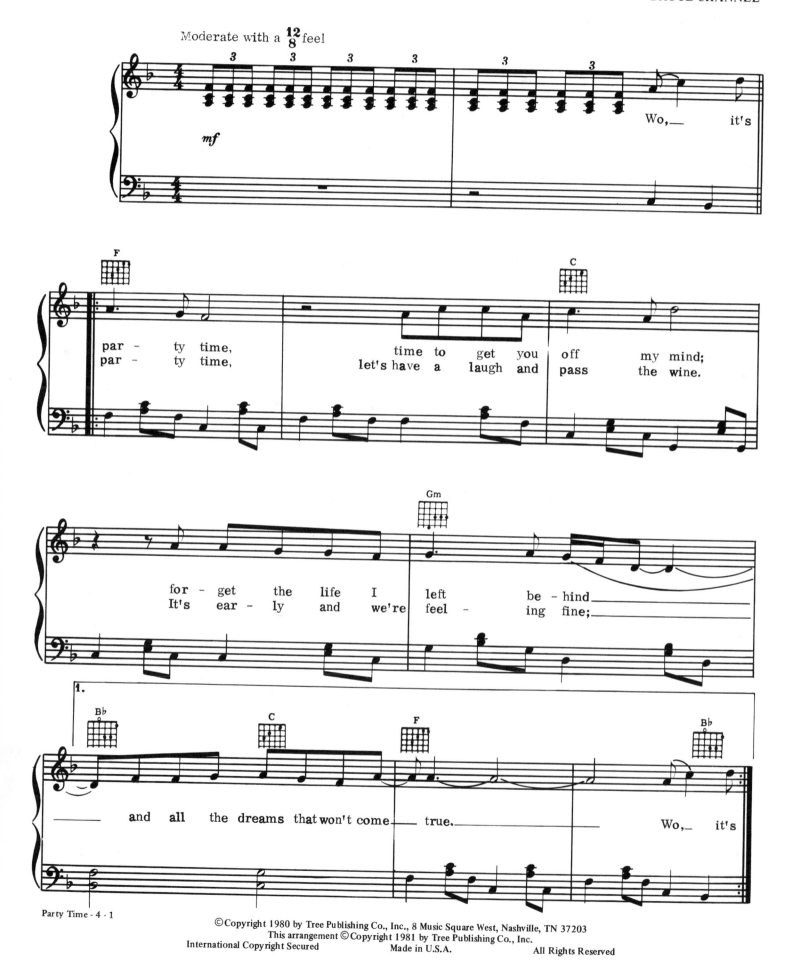

Party Time - 4 - 1

Party Time - 4 - 4

NOBODY IN HIS RIGHT MIND WOULD'VE LEFT HER

Words and Music by
DEAN DILLON

Nobody In His Right Mind Would've Left Her - 3 - 1

Verse 2:
I still carry her picture;
I wish her well with the new love
I know she's found by now.
Each night finds me dreaming;
Each day I spend thinking how much
I wish she was still around. *(To Chorus:)*

LOVE IS FAIR

Words and Music by
KYE FLEMING and
DENNIS W. MORGAN

Love Is Fair - 3 - 1

I can't blame you; you can't blame me; that's how love goes;____ it's no - bod - y's fault.

Chorus:

Love is fair,_____ I have dis - cov - ered;____ ____ it touch - es ev - 'ry - one one time or an - oth - er._____ Love is fair;____

Verse 2:
So it's goodbye; it was a good try;
And now we'll go our own way.
But if it helps, just remember
We're not the only ones to ever feel the pain.
(To Chorus:)

Love Is Fair - 3 - 3

FRIENDS

Words and Music by
JOHNNY SLATE and
DANNY MORRISON

Friends - 2 - 1

Chorus:

Friends, that's what we've been. is friends; through thick and thin__ we've been friends, and now love be - gins; and who makes bet - ter lov - ers than friends? who makes bet - ter lov - ers than who makes bet - ter lov - ers than friends? who makes bet - ter lov - ers

espr.

than friends?

molto rit.

Verse 2:
I never would have made it without you;
I almost waited too late to see
That all the time I was leaning on you,
You were leaning on me. *(To Chorus:)*

Verse 3:
Friends should always be something special;
You never know where friendship will lead.
We're sailing high on the sea of love,
And forever we'll be ... *To Chorus:)*

ANGEL FLYING TOO CLOSE
TO THE GROUND

Words and Music by
WILLIE NELSON

Angel Flying Too Close To The Ground - 4 - 1

Angel Flying Too Close To The Ground - 4 - 3

Angel Flying Too Close To The Ground - 4 - 4

GOOD TIMES

Words and Music by
WILLIE NELSON

1. When I
2. When I
3.4. *(see additional lyrics)*

ran to the store with a pen-ny,_____ and when
rolled rub-ber tires in the drive-way,_____ pulled a

youth was a-bun-dant and plen-ty;_____
purse on a string a-cross the high-way;_____

clas-si-fy these as good times,

Good Times - 2 - 1

Verse 3:
Go to school, fight a war, working steady;
Meet a girl, fall in love, for I'm ready;
Classify these as good times, good times.

Verse 4:
Here I sit with a drink and a memory,
But I'm not cold, I'm not wet, and I'm not hungry;
So classify these as good times, good times.
(To Chorus:)

Good Times - 2 - 2

THE CLOSER YOU GET

Words and Music by
MARK GRAY and
JAMES P. PENNINGTON

The Closer You Get - 2 - 1

GIRLS, WOMEN AND LADIES

Words and Music by
ED BRUCE, RON PETERSON
and PATSY BRUCE

Girls, Women And Ladies - 3 - 1

F

so I took the stool be - tween them; or-dered one more__

G **C**

round for me and her and him.

1. **2. 3.** *Chorus*:

F

2. I placed my And he said, "There's girls,_____ and there's

G **C** **F**

wom-en, and__there's la- -dies; there's yes - es,__ and there's

G **C** **F**

nos,_____ and there's may-bes; there's teas - ing, and

Girls, Women And Ladies - 3 - 2

Verse 2:
I placed my arm across the back of her bar stool;
And I don't remember what I said, but at the time it sounded cool.
She pushed her drink away, and never looked at me;
She just paid the tab, tipped the man,
And left me sitting there alone with him. *(To Chorus:)*

Verse 3:
Well, he pushed his old straw hat back, and he grinned;
And he said, "Ain't they all a mystery? Sonny, it's a sin;
But they're all sitting on the world we're trying to win;
Ah, but you know I love a mystery, so let's drink another round
To you and me and them." *(To Chorus:)*

DOESN'T ANYBODY GET HIGH
(On Love Anymore)

Words and Music by
AUSTIN ROBERTS and
JOHNNY CYMBAL

Doesn't anybody get high on love any more; on love any more?

1. Spending time, you're spending all your money shopping for a thrill; any old thing to chase those blues away.
2. I knew a man who made a million dollars, but he wanted more; know I've never seen that poor man smile.

Doesn't Anybody Get High - 3 - 1

Doesn't Anybody Get High - 3 - 2

Doesn't Anybody Get High - 3 - 3

UNWOUND

Words and Music by
DEAN DILLON and
FRANK DYCUS

Unwound - 3 - 1

WHEN IT'S JUST YOU AND ME

Easily ♩ = 100

Words and Music by
KENNY O'DELL

When It's Just You And Me - 3 - 1

When It's Just You And Me - 3 - 3

YOU ASKED ME TO

Words and Music by
WAYLON JENNINGS and
BILLY JOE SHAVER

You Asked Me To - 2 - 1

Chorus:

but if things are right with me and you,_____ that's all that mat-ters, and I'll do an-y-thing you asked me to.

1.3.4.5. and fade Let the world call me a *(2nd and 5th time guitar solo)*

2. 3. Know-ing how much I love *mp*

D.S.

Verse 3:
Knowing how much I love you,
And after all that I've been through,
I'd turn and walk away from you,
Just because you asked me to.

I REMEMBER YOU

Words by JOHNNY MERCER

Music by VICTOR SCHERTZINGER

I Remember You - 2 - 1

SOMETIME, SOMEWHERE, SOMEHOW

Moderately ♩ = 126

Words and Music by
JACK TURNER and
BRANT BEENE

Sometime, Somewhere, Somehow - 3 - 1

YOUR WIFE IS CHEATIN' ON US AGAIN

Words and Music by
WAYNE KEMP and
WARREN ROSS

1. Now old bud-dy, I'm not one to spread tales a-
2. (see additional lyrics)

round, but I fol-lowed your wife and an-

Your Wife Is Cheatin' On Us Again - 3 - 1

oth - er cow - boy to ev - 'ry honk-y tonk in town._____ Now

we've been friends through thick and thin; that's the least that I could

do; me and her's been pret-ty dang close,___ and there's

noth - in' I would - n't do for you; but

Chorus

your wife is cheat-in' on us a - gain.

Your Wife Is Cheatin' On Us Again - 3 - 2

Verse 2:
Now old buddy, you could be just a little better sport about this;
My poor old eyes is gettin' sore from poundin' on your fist;
So let's shake hands and call it quits, and go kick in that cowboy's door.
We'll show them a thing or two, if you'll let me off this floor.
(To Chorus:)

Your Wife Is Cheatin' On Us Again - 3 - 3

THE MATADOR

Words and Music by
DON PFRIMMER and
BOB MORRIS

The Matador - 3 - 1

Verse 4:
As I watch his body turn and twist,
He doesn't know that I exist;
Though I've shared so many dreams before with the matador.

Verse 6:
And as he leaves the ring, they cheer;
Sombreros fly into the air;
And I throw the crimson rose I wore to the matador.
(To Coda:)

The Matador - 3 - 3

HILLBILLY GIRL WITH THE BLUES

Words and Music by
LACY J. DALTON

Friends, I know darn well___ that I'm head - ed straight for hell,___ if I
2. *(see additional lyrics)*

keep on liv-ing the cra - zy way I do; but I

real - ly have to say___ I've come a long, long way___ for___ a

Hillbilly Girl With The Blues - 3 - 1

Verse 2:
Someday soon I'll settle down in some quiet little town;
And I won't look back 'til I leave these blues behind.
I'm gonna play my old guitar; praise the Lord, and pass the jar;
I'm gonna sing myself a little piece of mind.
Don't you know these city lights can really blind a country girl;
People offer things she's too green to refuse;
But there's ... *(To Coda)*

Hillbilly Girl With The Blues - 3 - 3

HUSBANDS AND WIVES

Words and Music by
ROGER MILLER

Husbands And Wives - 3 - 1

wom-an and ___ a man; a man and a wom-an; some can and

some can't; ___ and some ___ can't. ___

espr.

D.S. al Coda 𝄋

wives.

espr.

rit.

p

Coda

SINCE I DON'T HAVE YOU

Words by
JAMES BEAUMONT, JANET VOGEL,
JOSEPH VERSCHAREN,
WALTER LESTER and JOHN TAYLOR

Music by
JOSEPH ROCK and
LENNIE MARTIN

Since I Don't Have You - 3 - 1

IT'S A HEARTACHE

Words and Music by
RONNIE SCOTT and
STEVE WOLFE

It's A Heartache - 3 - 1

It ain't right with love to share,___ when you find___ he does-n't care___ for you.

It ain't wise to need some - one___ as much as I de-pend-ed on ___ you. 4. Oh, it's a

CODA

Oh, it's a heart - ache, ___ noth - ing but a
fool's game, ___ noth - ing but a

heart - ache. ___ You love him 'till your arms break, ___
fool's game, ___ stand - ing in the cold rain, ___

then ___ he'll let you down. ___ It's a
feel - ing like a clown. ___

Repeat ad lib and Fade

It's A Heartache - 3 - 3

LOVE AIN'T NEVER HURT NOBODY

Words and Music by
BOBBY GOLDSBORO

Love Ain't Never Hurt Nobody - 3 - 2

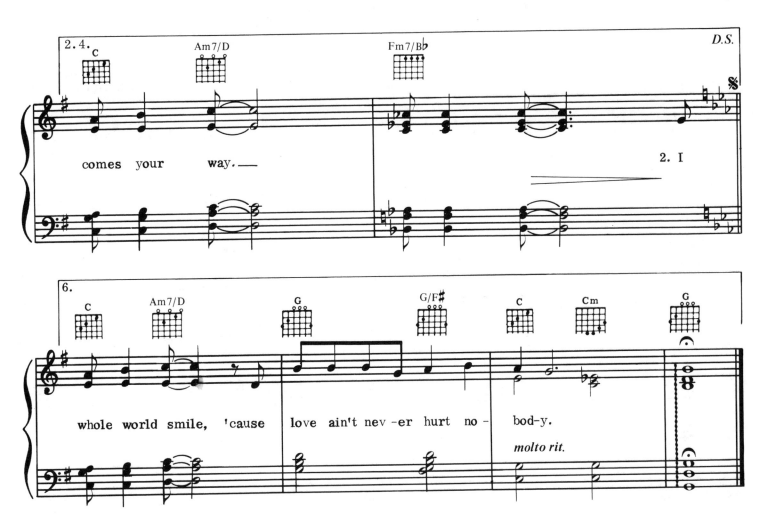

comes your way. — 2. I

whole world smile, 'cause love ain't nev-er hurt no-bod-y.

molto rit.

Verse 2:
I heard a lady say that love's a foolish game;
She was crying 'cause her man had gone away;
But that lady's only got herself to blame,
'Cause love isn't something that you play.
(To Chorus:)

Verse 3:
A little love can bring us all together,
If we will only open up our hearts.
(To Chorus:)

WISH YOU WERE HERE

Easily ♩ = 100

Words and Music by
KYE FLEMING and
DENNIS MORGAN

1.I took a va-ca-tion down by the o-cean,
2.3.5.(see additional lyrics) 4.(Instr. solo ad lib)

but it's no fun with a heart that's bro-ken; ooh ba - by, ___

I wish you were here. ___

2. I

I (end solo)

Chorus:

wish you were here, ___ I've got to be hon-est, it's no fun a-lone ___ drink-ing

Wish You Were Here - 2 - 1

Verse 2:
I see lovers walking on the beach at sunset;
I turn to you, I guess I'm just in the habit;
Ooh baby, I wish you were here.

Verse 3:
If I knew where you were, I'd send you a postcard;
Having a blue time, I'm so lonely so far;
Ooh baby, I wish you were here.

Verse 5:
I put on my gown, I turned all my lights out;
Pulled back the covers, I'm going to bed now;
Ooh baby, I wish you were here.
(To Coda:)

Wish You Were Here - 2 - 2

EVERY NOW AND THEN

Words and Music by
SHAYNE DOLAN and
ROCK KILLOUGH

Every Now And Then - 2 - 1

Verse 3:
Someday I'll find the one who's meant for me,
And I know that someday you'll find love again;
But we'll always have a very special memory
Of the love we gave each other now and then.

Every Now And Then - 2 - 2

I CAN'T HOLD MYSELF IN LINE

Words and Music by
MERLE HAGGARD

Moderately

mf

mp

D   A7   D

1.4. I'm go-ing off of the deep end_____ and

2.5. *(see additional lyrics)* 3. *(Instr. solo ad lib)*

D   A7   G7

I'm slow-ly los-in' my mind._____ Well, I

I Can't Hold Myself In Line - 2 - 1

don't like me, and the way that I'm liv-in',____ but

I can't hold ____ my-self in line. ____

Verse 2:
You know, I give nobody no excuses for my drinking,
But my woman is still my best friend;
But if I don't change, I know I'm gonna lose her,
But I can't hold myself in line.

Verse 5:
Lord, we can't hold ourselves in line;
I guess we can't hold ourselves in line;
I'm full speed ahead down the wrong road of life,
'Cause we can't hold ourselves in line.

I Can't Hold Myself In Line - 2 - 2

WANDERING EYES

Words and Music by
JAMIE O'HARA

JUST GOT BACK FROM NO MANS LAND

Easily ♩ = 76

Words and Music by
DANNY WALLS

Just Got Back From No Mans Land - 2 - 1

Just Got Back From No Man s Land - 2 - 2

STILL DOIN' TIME

Words and Music by
MICHAEL P. HEENEY and
JOHN E. MOFFAT

Still Doin' Time - 3 - 1

Still Doin' Time - 3 - 2

IT'S ALL I CAN DO

Words and Music by
RICHARD LEIGH and
ARCHIE JORDAN

1. It's been a-while;— how have you been?—
2. To see the lips I used to kiss,—

It's real-ly good,— you know,— to see you a-gain.—
does-n't make it eas-y to just stand here like this.—

You'd think by now those old feel-ings had died,— but it on-ly takes.
I get to think-ing I'm do-ing all right,— then I see the arms.

It's All I Can Do - 3 - 1

It's all I can do to keep this heart from just break-

ing in two.

it's all I can do to keep this heart from just break-

ing in two.

It's All I Can Do - 3 - 3

CAN I SEE YOU TONIGHT

Words and Music by
RAFE VANHOY and
DEBORAH ALLEN

Moderately ♩ = 126

(Instr. solo ad lib)

(end solo)

1. I don't know where to start, now that we've fall - en a - part;
2. I've tried to un - der - stand but things got so out of hand;
3. 4. (see additional lyrics)

I've how can we talk heart to heart; you're so
held out as long as I can; and

far a - way, what can we say?
now I'm on the tel - - e - phone say - ing,

Can I See You Tonight - 2 - 1

149

Verse 3: Now that we're on the line,
I'll tell you what's on my mind;
The love that we're trying to hide;
Well, it's suffering from too much pride.

Verse 4: When will we see the end
To this game where nobody wins;
'Cause as long as nobody gives in,
It goes on and on and on and on.
(To Chorus:)

Can I See You Tonight - 2 - 2

WHAT IN THE WORLD'S COME OVER YOU

Words and Music by
JACK SCOTT

Slowly (strict beat)

WHAT IN THE WORLD'S COME O - VER YOU? Seems we nev - er — get a-long; Ev - 'ry night I rem - i - nisce, Dream-ing of your ten - der kiss - es; WHAT IN THE WORLD'S COME O - VER YOU? Will you ev - er — change your mind? If you do, I'll still be here, dear, wait-ing, long-ing for you.

What In The World's Come Over You - 2 1

What In The World's Come Over You - 2 - 2

STORMS NEVER LAST

Words and Music by
JESSI COLTER

Moderately

Chorus:

Storms nev - er_____ last, do they ba - by?
3. *(Instr. solo ad lib)*

Bad times all pass with the wind.

Storms Never Last - 3 - 1

Your hand in mine＿＿ stills the thun - der,

and you'd make＿ the sun＿＿ want to shine.

no repeat 1st time

I've fol - lowed you down so man - y roads,

Storms Never Last - 3 - 2

ba - by.____ I've picked wild____ flowers____ and sung you soft, sad

songs. And ev - 'ry road we took,____ God knows____ our

search was for the truth,____ and the storm____ that's brew - ing now____

D.S. repeat chorus ad lib and fade 𝄋

____ won't____ be the last.

Storms Never Last - 3 - 3

YOU'VE GOT A GOOD LOVE COMING

Words and Music by
DANNY MORRISON, VAN STEPHENSON
and JEFF SILBAR

Moderately ♩.= 80

1. Look out,__ there's a sun-ny day;__ I do be-lieve__ it's
2. Knock knock,_ ba-by, guess who's here? I've come to make__

head-ed your__ way.__ You've been cry-ing__
one thing_ clear._ No more heart-aches,_

long e-nough,__ but you'll for-get what a tear-drop was,__ 'cause
no more fears,_ to-night's the night they're gon-na dis-ap-pear,__ 'cause

You've Got A Good Love Coming - 3 - 1

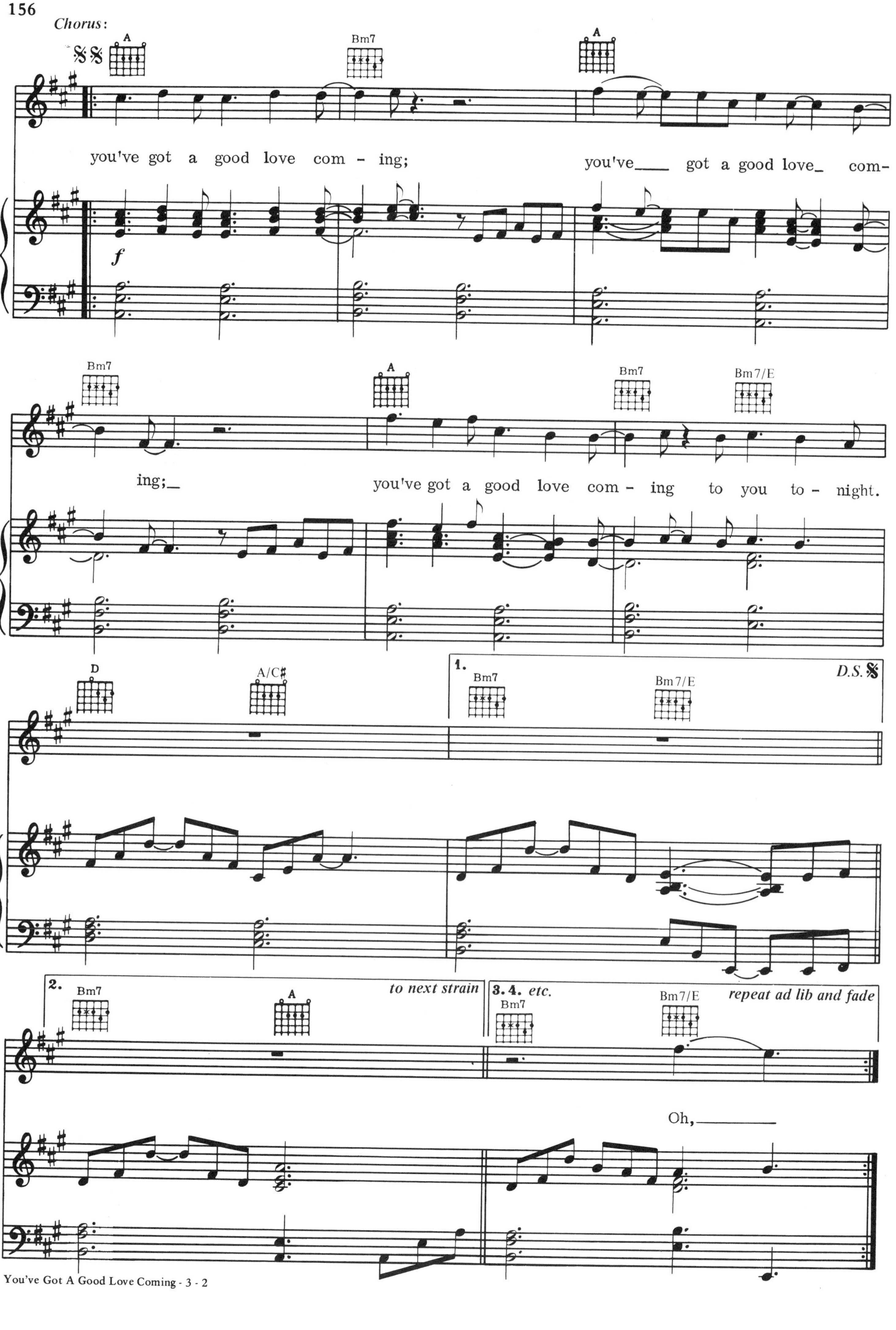
Chorus:
A
Bm7
A
you've got a good love com - ing;
you've___ got a good love_ com-
f
Bm7
A
Bm7
Bm7/E
ing;_
you've got a good love com - ing to you to - night.
D
A/C♯
1.
Bm7
Bm7/E
D.S.
2.
Bm7
A
to next strain
3. 4. etc.
Bm7
Bm7/E
repeat ad lib and fade
Oh,___

You've Got A Good Love Coming - 3 - 3

STAND BY YOUR MAN

By
TAMMY WYNETTE and
BILLY SHERRILL

Stand By Your Man - 2 - 1

OLDER WOMEN

Words and Music by
JAMIE O'HARA

RUN TO HER

Moderately ♩. = 88

Words and Music by
GERRY GOFFIN and
JACK KELLER

1. If you've found an-oth-er girl who sat-is-fies you more than I do, run to her; I'll step__ a-side. And

Run To Her - 3 - 1

if you think her lips can kiss you bet-ter than my lips can kiss you,

2. If some-bod-y else can make you hap-pi-er than I can make you,

3. (Instr. solo)

run to her; for-get___ my pride.___
run to her; my tears___ will dry.___

Oh, if some-one else-'s arms can hold you bet-ter than my arms can hold you,

go to her;___ and___ show___ to her

all your___ de-vo-tion.

1st time D.S. 𝄋
2nd time D.S. al Coda 𝄋

Run To Her - 3 - 2

DOWN AND OUT

Words and Music by
DEAN DILLON and
FRANK DYCUS

Down And Out - 3 - 1

Verse 2:
I'm down to my last dollar, but I don't really care.
My friends have all got whiskey and they don't mind if I share.
They know how it feels to have your heart torn inside out;
And since my woman left I'm down and out.
(To Chorus:)

Down And Out - 3 - 3

HOLD ME LIKE YOU NEVER HAD ME

Words and Music by
ROBERT BYRNE and
TOM BRASFIELD

1. Late-ly when you love_ me,_____ it seems so_____ cut and dried;
2. Bod-ies grow fa - mil - iar,_____no sur - pris - es_____ an - y - more;

ba - by, I get lone - ly when I'm lay - ing by your side._____
like an old late mov-ie show, you've seen it all be - fore;_____

If you need a fan - ta - sy_____ to keep you_____ sat-is - fied,
but it's a clas-sic sto - ry,_____ the good ones_____ nev-er die;

Hold Me Like You Never Had Me - 3 - 1

Hold Me Like You Never Had Me - 3 - 3

EVERYONE GETS CRAZY NOW AND THEN

Words and Music by
KEVIN WELCH

Everyone Gets Crazy Now And Then - 3 - 1

Everyone Gets Crazy Now And Then - 3 - 2

Verse 2:
Yes, I know those empty nights get lonely;
Sometimes you feel like you're the only one to lose more than he wins.
Yes, these troubled times get scary, but that's just ordinary;
Everyone gets crazy now and then.

Verse 3:
Sometimes I get crazy, just like you;
Get feeling lost and lonely too, like some old flag left flying in the wind.
Time has taught me this for sure, time itself is the only cure;
(To Coda)

SECRETS

Words and Music by
SAM LORBER, MIKE NOBLE,
JEFF SILBAR and MAC DAVIS

1. Can't be no se-crets
2. (see additional lyric)

if we're gon-na last; ___ can't keep an-y-thing from ___

___ me; fu-ture, pre-sent, or past; ___

Secrets - 3 - 1

Secrets - 3 - 2

be - tween you and me,

oh.

1. D.S. **2.** D.S.S. **3.**

repeat ad lib and fade

(bkgr.) Se - crets; se - crets.
(lead vocal ad lib)

mf

Verse 2:
Hidden truth or fantasy;
Got nothing to hide;
Come on and open up for me;
Let me come inside;
What I don't know haunts me;
What you don't say burns;
There's nothing you can show me that'll shock me;
Nothing I don't want to learn.
(To Chorus:)

MISS EMILY'S PICTURE

Moderately ♩ = 120

Words and Music by
RED LANE

1. I wake up in the morn-ing in a state of fright; on the
2.3.4. (see additional lyrics)

wrong side of the bed___ all night, cling-ing to the bro- ken heart in-

side my head.___ O-pen my eyes and I move my hand___

Miss Emily's Picture - 3 - 1

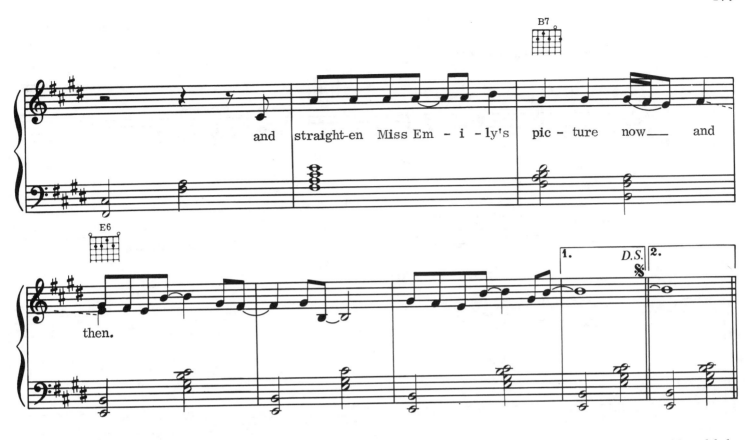

and straight-en Miss Em - i -ly's pic - ture now___ and

then.

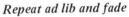

Repeat ad lib and fade

Verse 2:
Go to the office, the work's piled up;
Pour three fingers bourbon in my coffee cup,
And cry on my best friend's shoulder down the hall;
Feels so lonely when I close the door;
Bite my nails and I walk the floor,
And straighten Miss Emily's picture on my wall.

Verse 3:
I leave my office and I go downtown
To a little bar we all hang around;
Laugh, drink beer, and shoot pool and have a ball.
When the laughter stops and the hurt takes hold;
Reach in my pocket for my billfold,
And show Miss Emily's picture to them all.

Verse 4:
I stagger in the house and I slam the door;
Scatter my clothes all over the floor;
Wishin' I could do the same thing in my head.
Drink a beer and I eat a bite,
And just before I turn out the lights
I straighten Miss Emily's picture by my bed.

Miss Emily's Picture - 3 - 3

OLD FLAME

Words and Music by
DONNY LOWERY and
MAC McANALLY

Old Flame - 2 - 1

WHISPER

Words and Music by
LACY J. DALTON and
MARK SHERRILL

Whisper - 2 - 1

Whisper - 2 - 2

DRIFTER

Words and Music by
ARCHIE JORDAN and
DON PFRIMMER

Verse 3:
Drifter, please remember,
No one loves you like I do.

Verse 5:
Drifter, I'll be waiting
Should you ever drift back in.

Verse 6:
Drifter, oh drifter,
(To Coda:)

WHAT I HAD WITH YOU

Words and Music by
CURLY PUTMAN and
SONNY THROCKMORTON

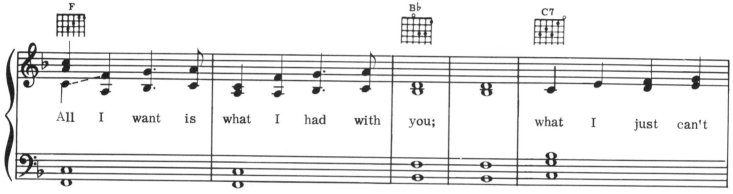

All I want is what I had with you; what I just can't

find with some-one new; I've tried oth - er loves, but they won't

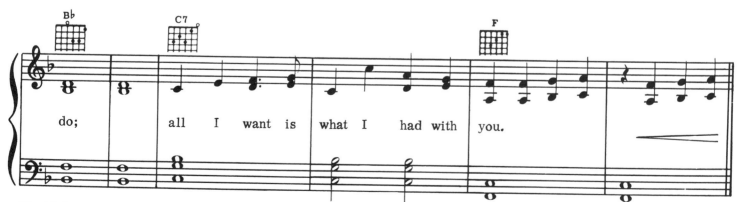

do; all I want is what I had with you.

What I Had With You - 2 - 1

Look - ing back in time, I see yes - ter- day;

when I held the whole world,_____ then let it slip a - way._____

_____ Chang-ing times, and strange new loves just leave me blue;

all I want is what I had with you.

you.

HIDE-A-WAY HEALING

Words and Music by
OSCAR SOLOMON and
STEPHANIE WINSLOW

1. All week long, we've been talk-ing it
2. (see additional lyrics)

o - ver___ with words so hot they burn the tel - e - phone

lines; the time is right for us to get to -

geth - er;___ I'll mend your bro-ken heart while you're mend-ing mine.___ We've got that

Hide-A-Way Healing - 2 - 1

Verse 2:
I know she's been putting the hurt on you again;
You know he's been doing the same to me.
We're long overdue, and we owe it to each other,
And now we're as ready as we'll ever be.
We've got that ... *(To Chorus:)*

ROLL ON MISSISSIPPI

Words and Music by
KYE FLEMING and
DENNIS W. MORGAN

1. Walk-ing a-long,___ whis-tling a song,___ bare-foot, and fan-
2. Cool riv-er breeze,___ like pep-per-mint leaves,___ the taste of it takes___
3. *(see additional lyrics)*

cy free;___ a big riv-er boat___ pass-ing us by,___
me back;___ chew-ing on straw,___ torn o-ver-alls,

___ she's head-ed for New___ Or-leans.___ There she goes,
___ cane pole and old___ straw hat;___ mud-dy riv-er,

Roll On Mississippi - 3 - 1

dis - ap - pear- ing a-round the bend;
just like a long lost friend;

roll on Mis - sis-

sip - pi; you make me feel like a child a - gain.

a - gain.

Roll on Mis - sis-

Chorus:

sip - pi; big riv - er roll;

you're the child - hood dream I grew up on.

Roll On Mississippi - 3 - 2

Verse 3:
When the world's spinning 'round too fast for me,
I need a place to dream;
So I come to your banks, I sit in your shade
And relive the memories:
Tom Sawyer and Huckleberry Finn;
Roll on Mississippi; you make me feel like a child again.
(To Chorus:)

NEVER BEEN SO LOVED
(In All My Life)

Words and Music by
WAYLAND HOLYFIELD and
NORRIS WILSON

Never Been So Loved - 3 - 1

194

Never Been So Loved - 3 - 2

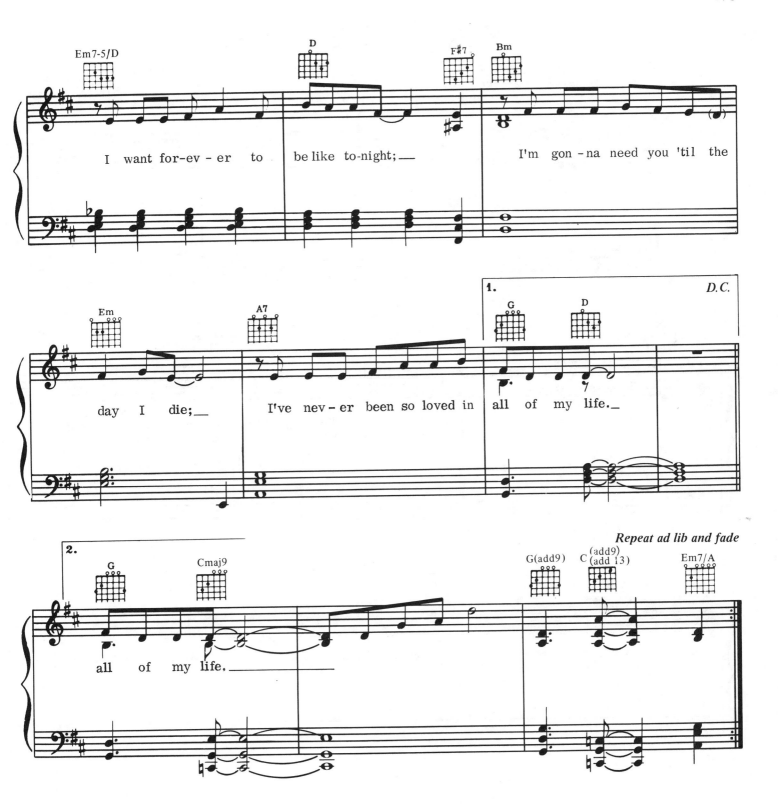

Verse 3:
Simply amazing, you're naturally fine;
You've got a hold on this heart of mine;
And I don't want you to ever let go;
I just want you to know,
(To Chorus:)

YOU'RE THE BEST

Words and Music by
KIERAN KANE and
BRUCE CHANNEL

You're The Best - 2 - 1

HEART ON THE MEND

Words and Music by
KYE FLEMING and
DENNIS W. MORGAN

Heart On The Mend - 2 - 1

Chorus:
Heart ___ on the mend; ___ time is the ___ best med-i-cine ___ there is. ___

Heart ___ on the mend; ___ a cou-ple

hun-dred years, ___ and I'll be read-y to love a - gain.

1. D.S.   2. To next strain

3.4.etc.   Repeat ad lib and fade

I'm pick-ing up the piec - es, ___ get-ting o - ver you; ___

___ a lit-tle time ___ and I'll ___ be good as new.   Oh, ___   D.S.S.

Verse 2:
I saw you in the doorway with somebody new;
You said hello but I just danced on by.
I bet you thought I'd break down, just like I used to;
But I fooled you and held it all inside.
(To Chorus:)

WE DON'T HAVE TO HOLD OUT

Words and Music by
AIDAN MASON and
GORD ADAMS

We Don't Have To Hold Out - 4 - 1

We don't have to stay out in the cold an-y-more;

let's just take this chance and nev - er let it go.

Now we could hide a - way, live our lives a - lone,

We Don't Have To Hold Out - 4 - 3

WHO'S CHEATIN' WHO

Lively ♩ = 132

Words and Music by
JERRY HAYES

Ev - 'ry-where you look,
2.4. (see additional lyrics)
3. (Instr. solo)
you can write a book on the trou-ble with a wom-an and a

man;___ but you can not im-pose; you can't stick your nose in-to

some-thing that you don't___ un-der-stand. Still you won-der

Repeat 3rd time only

Who's Cheatin' Who - 2 - 1

Verse 2:
I thought I knew him well; I really couldn't tell
That he had another lover on his mind.
You see it felt so right when he held me tight;
How could I be so blind?
But still you wonder ... *(To Chorus:)*

Verse 4:
A heart is on the line each and every time
Love is stolen in the shadows of the night.
Though it's wrong all along, it keeps going on
As long as they keep out of sight.
But still you wonder ... *(To Chorus:)*

ALICE DOESN'T LOVE HERE ANYMORE

Words and Music by
BOBBY GOLDSBORO

Alice Doesn't Love Here Anymore - 3 - 1

Alice Doesn't Love Here Anymore - 3 - 2

Verse 3: She cleans the breakfast dishes, and thinks about her wishes;
The dreams she had when she was just a girl;
How one day she would marry, have a husband and a family;
That's all that seemed to matter in the world.

Verse 4: But inside there's still a hunger, and she's not getting any younger;
And she feels that there must be something more.
The feeling's growing stronger, and she can't fake it any longer;
'Cause Alice doesn't love here anymore. *(To Chorus:)*

Chorus 2: She thinks about her family, and how she's gonna tell them;
Will they understand why she just had to go?
And when the neighbors ask what happened, will they find it hard to tell them
That Alice doesn't love here anymore?

Verse 5: When tomorrow comes around, the circus comes to town;
And he's gonna take the children for the day.
She'll say it's now or never, and she'll get her things together;
She'll dry her eyes and quickly drive away. *(To Chorus:)*

Chorus 3: And when the carnival is over and they all come home together;
They'll find this note that she left on the door;
"If the phone should ring and someone asks to speak to Alice,
Just say Alice doesn't love here anymore."

Alice Doesn't Love Here Anymore - 3 - 3

TRUE LIFE COUNTRY MUSIC

Words and Music by
DANNY MORRISON, JEFF SILBAR
and SAM LORBE

True Life Country Music - 3 - 2

Verse 2:
In a barroom in Toledo, with a girl they call Lucille;
On a train bound for nowhere, I watched the gambler deal;
Spent the night in Detroit City, you were gentle on my mind;
Down country roads, so far from home, so lonesome I could cry.
(To Chorus:)

Verse 3:
I know every man in Fulsom, every trucker who can't sleep;
Been a prayer for a wino, who dreamed of satin sheets.
I rode with Roy Acuff on The Wabash Cannonball;
I'm true life country music and I guess I've seen it all.
(To Chorus:)

I WANNA BE AROUND

Words and Music by
JOHNNY MERCER and
SADIE VIMMERSTEDT

I Wanna Be Around - 2 - 1

I Wanna Be Around - 2 - 2

SMOKY MOUNTAIN RAIN

Words and Music by
KYE FLEMING and
DENNIS MORGAN

Easily ♩ = 69

espr.

p

I thumbed my way from L. A. back to Knox-ville;   I found   out those bright lights

2. *(see additional lyrics)*

ain't where __ I be-long. __   From a phone booth, in the rain, __

__ I called to tell her   I've had a change of dreams, __

Smoky Mountain Rain - 3 - 1

215

Smoky Mountain Rain - 3 - 2

216

Verse 2:
I waved a diesel down outside a cafe;
He said that he was going as far as Gatlinburg.
I climbed up in the cab, all wet, and cold, and lonely;
I wiped my eyes and told him about her.
I've got to find her, can you make these big wheels burn?
(To Chorus:)

Smoky Mountain Rain - 3 - 3

CHEATING IS STILL ON MY MIND

Words and Music by
ROBERT JENKINS

Cheating Is Still On My Mind - 3 - 1

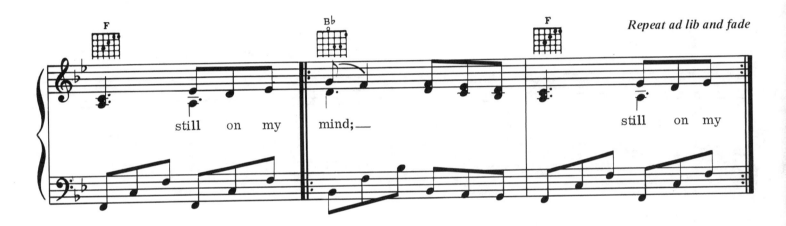

Verse 2:
We meet at a rendezvous table for two;
Over and over I'm dancing with you.
I whisper I love you and you reach out your hand;
When I open my eyes, I'm dreaming again,
I'm dreaming again.
(To Chorus:)

Verse 3:
Maybe I'm going through some kind of stage;
I feel like I'm chained, locked in a cage.
The excitement you offer is tempting to me,
But I've never cheated, except in my dreams,
Except in my dreams.
(To Chorus:)

HE'S THE FIRE

Words and Music by
DANNY MORRISON and
CHESTER LESTER

He's The Fire - 2 - 1

Verse 3:
My body feels the splendor of his hands so warm and tender,
As his gentle lips feed my hungry soul;
I've tried so hard to fight it, but now I've been ignited,
And in his arms I burn out of control.
(To Chorus:)

He's The Fire - 2 - 2

MIDNIGHT HAULER

Words and Music by
TIM DuBOIS and
WOOD NEWTON

1.5. Well, it's

eight-een wheels roll-ing heav-y through the des-ert night;

2.3.(see additional lyrics)
4.6.7. (inst. solo ad lib)

I been driv-ing all day, but I won't shut her down to-

Midnight Hauler - 3 - 1

Verse 2:
Got my load strapped down and my Peter built's wound up tight;
I got my saddles full of diesel and my belly's full of coffee and whites;
Well, I'm talkin' on the radio; keepin' track of old Smokey Joe,
'Cause the Midnight Hauler is cannonballin' her home.

Verse 3:
I got a little woman waitin' back in old K.C.;
That sweet, gentle woman don't love nobody but me;
I just called her on the telephone;
I said tomorrow night she won't sleep alone,
'Cause the Midnight Hauler is cannonballin' her home.
(To Bridge:)

I WAS COUNTRY
WHEN COUNTRY WASN'T COOL

Words and Music by
KYE FLEMING and
DENNIS W. MORGAN

I Was Country When Country Wasn't Cool - 3 - 1

Verse 2:
I remember circling the drive-in,
Pulling up, and turning down George Jones.
I remember when no one was looking,
I was putting peanuts in my coke.
I took a lot of kidding, 'cause I never did fit in;
Now look at everybody trying to be what I was then;
I was country, when country wasn't cool.

Verse 3:
They called us country bumpkins for sticking to our roots;
I'm just glad we're in a country where we're all free to choose;
I was country, when country wasn't cool.

I Was Country When Country Wasn't Cool - 3 - 3

I'VE BEEN WAITING FOR YOU ALL OF MY LIFE

Words and Music by
LINDA KIMBALL and
MARK SHERRILL

I've Been Waiting For You All Of My Life - 3 - 1

I've Been Waiting For You All Of My Life - 3 - 2

I've wait-ed for you all__ my life.

life. I've been wait-ing for you

life. I've been wait-ing for you; wait-ed for you all of my

life._____

I LOVED 'EM EVERY ONE

Words and Music by
PHIL SAMPSON

1. I've known some paint-ed la - dies___ that spar - kled in the light;___
2. Some I nev - er real - ly knew,_____ though I al - ways want - ed to;___
3. - 6. (see additional lyrics)

coun-try girls that loved the lov - er's moon.___
some I on - ly met once in a room.

I Loved 'Em Every One - 3 - 1

I Loved 'Em Every One - 3 - 2

Verse 3:
Some said they liked my smile.
Others of 'em stayed awhile;
While others left me on the run.

Verse 4:
This is the only way;
Only way I have to say,
Mm, I loved 'em every one. *(To Chorus:)*

Verse 5:
Here's to the ladies
In saloons, and living rooms;
Summer nights that lasted until dawn.

Verse 6:
Here's to the memories;
Every one's a part of me;
Oh, I loved 'em every one.
(To Chorus:)

I Loved 'Em Every One - 3 - 3

BEDTIME STORIES

Words and Music by
DANNY MORRISON and
CHESTER LESTER

1. Well, he's
3. He's al-

2. watch-ing T. V. and he don't e-ven see as she reach-es to turn out the
2. e-ven sus-pi-cious that some-one and his Mrs. have been out all day a-
3.4. (see additional lyrics)

light; he don't her hand is shak-ing, she said her head is ach-ing; it's the
lone; he thinks she's a-bove it, and to-think noth-in' of it, he

same lie she told him last night. 2. He's not day she just beat him home. Those

Chorus: C

bed - time sto-ries hide it so well; what { she's / he's / they've

Verse 3:
He's already asleep but she's still counting sheep,
'Cause she can't keep the day off her mind;
And if she only knew he was cheating her too,
Sleep would be easy to find.

Verse 4:
But the truth is she don't,
And he's betting she won't
Find out he's doing her wrong;
He thinks it's all right
To lie to her every night,
'Cause he's been at it so long.
(To Chorus:)

I AM THE DREAMER
(You Are The Dream)

Words and Music by
DAVE HALL, RUSS ALLISON
and DALLAS CODY

Moderately Bright ♩= 88

kiss in the dark; _____ the touch of your hand; _____ my
2. (see additional lyrics)

arms are a-round _____ you; my dream be-gins. _____ The

on-ly thing that's dif-fer-ent than an-y oth-er night; _____

here we are to-geth - er, my dream by my side. _____

1. A

I Am The Dreamer - 2 - 1

Chorus:

I am the dream - er, you are the dream;

you are the an - swer to my fan - ta - sy. All that I have

dreamed of, now is com - plete; I am the dream - er,

you are the dream. 2. I

dream. dream.

Repeat ad lib and fade

Verse 2:
I know that I've been dreamin', but I finally saw the light;
With my arms wide open, I found a love that's right.
You don't have to wake me, for me to know it's real;
The love that I have dreamed of, I can touch and feel.
(To Chorus:)

AM I LOSING YOU?

Words and Music by
JIM REEVES

Verses 3. & 5:
Will the sweet things you do
Be for somebody new?
Tell me what to do;
Am I losing you?

SOME DAYS ARE DIAMONDS
(Some Days Are Stone)

Words and Music by
DICK FELLER

Some Days Are Diamonds - 3 - 1

GOOD OL' GIRLS

Words and Music by
DAN WILSON

Good Ol' Girls - 3 - 1

Good Ol' Girls - 3 - 2

Verse 2:
Well, you can bet them boys ain't sittin' there drinking
Just to pass away the time;
And the pinball players and the eight ball shooters
Got another game on their mind.
It's a simple thing, just take a look;
It's the same all over the world.
There wouldn't be one single good ol' boy
If it wasn't for the good ol' girls. (To Chorus:)

Verse 3:
You can look into their faces,
And just about read their minds;
Good ol' boys hate being alone
When it comes to closing time.
They live for the night life,
Cold beer, and a good ol' country song;
But there's just one thing that keeps 'em out running,
Instead of staying at home, and that's ... (To Chorus:)

IT WASN'T GOD WHO MADE HONKY TONK ANGELS

Words and Music by
J.D. MILLER

It Wasn't God Who Made Honky Tonk Angels - 2 - 1

It Wasn't God Who Made Honky Tonk Angels - 2 - 2

WHEN YOU FALL IN LOVE, EVERYTHING'S A WALTZ

Words and Music by
ED BRUCE, PATSY BRUCE
and RON PETERSON

When You Fall In Love, Everything's A Waltz - 2 - 1

When You Fall In Love, Everything's A Waltz - 2 - 2

I LOVE A RAINY NIGHT

Moderately Bright ♩. = 132

Words and Music by
EDDIE RABBITT, EVEN STEVENS
and DAVID MALLOY

1.3. Well, I love_____ a rain-y night; I love a rain-y night. I
2.4. _____ a rain-y night; it's such a beau-ti-ful sight. I love to
5. *(Instr. solo ad lib)*

love to hear the thun-der; watch the light-ning when it lights up____ the sky.____
feel ____ the rain on my face; ____ taste the rain on____ my lips, ____

1. 3.
You know it makes_ me feel_____ good.__

2.4.5.
2. Well, I love_

in the moon-light shad - ows.__

(end solo)

I Love A Rainy Night - 2 - 1

Bridge:

1.3. Show-ers wash___ all my cares a - way;___ I wake up___ to a
2. Puts a song___ in this heart of mine;___ puts a smile___ on my

Chorus:

sun - ny day,___ 'cause I love___ a rain - y night. Yeah, I love___
face ev - 'ry time,___

___ a rain - y night. Well, I love___ a rain - y night. Well, I love___

___ a rain - y night, ooh, ooh. I love___ a rain - y night. Well, I love___

Repeat ad lib and fade (vocal ad lib)

I Love A Rainy Night - 2 - 2

CHICKEN TRUCK

Words and Music by
ERVAN JAMES PARKER,
MONROE FIELDS and
JOHN ANDERSON

Chicken Truck - 3 - 1

chick-en truck_ from Geor - gia, and the

feath-ers was a - fly - in' like snow out of the sky.

1.3.

2.4.

Chorus:

Chick-en truck, chick-en truck; be - hind it I'm stuck; chick-en

truck, chick-en truck; it's just my luck; chick-en truck, chick-en truck, on

High - way Six - ty - five. Well, the

Chicken Truck - 3 - 2

Verse 2:
I couldn't get up the speed enough to pass him,
And a funny smell was gettin' close to me;
And something keeps on messin' up my windshield,
And the further I go, the harder it gets to see.
(To Chorus:)

Verse 4:
Then he slowed down and I finally got around him,
On a big, long hill just south of Tennessee.
He had a box of Colonel Sanders on his dashboard,
And he was eatin' fried chicken and throwin' his bones on me.
(To Chorus:)

ARE YOU HAPPY BABY

Words and Music by
BOB STONE

Sometimes I won-der if ___ you ev-er knew ___ how much you were
Some friends of yours and mine ___ say late-ly, things ___ with you ain't ___

hurt - ing me.
been ___ so good.

You fell in love with ___ some-one
I told you I would ___ nev - er

else, and ___ just like that, you de - sert - ed me.
take you ___ back a - gain, but you know ___ I would.

I have-n't seen you ___ for so long; ___ thought I'd
Does - n't mat - ter ___ an - y more ___ who was

call; ___ I won - der, are you ___ hap - py
wrong; ___ I won - der, are you ___ hap - py

Are You Happy Baby - 3 - 2

Are You Happy Baby - 3 - 3

IT WAS YOU

Words and Music by
BOB HOUSE and
BILLY STONE

It Was You - 2 - 1

It Was You - 2 - 2

SCRATCH MY BACK
(And Whisper In My Ear)

Words and Music by
MARCELL STRONG,
RAYMOND MOORE and
EARL CAGE, Jr.

Scratch My Back - 2 - 1

Verse 2:
You've got fingertips so gentle
When they go strolling down my back.
Your sweet and sexy voice in my ear
Makes my whole body relax.

You've got that sweet and gentle feelin';
Girl, let it last forever and a day;
And if you decide to leave me
You might as well take my whole life away.
It's got to be the way you ... *(Chorus)*

Scratch My Back - 2 - 2

COUNTRYFIED

Words and Music by
DANNY HOGAN and
RONNY SCAIFE

1. Look-ing at a
2.3.(see additional lyrics)

frog eat-ing up my fish bait, sit-ting on the bank of a riv-er-side;___ took a lit-tle

drink from a jug of moon-shine, did-n't have a chas-er, and al-most died.___ Think-ing 'bout

work-ing on Mon-day morn-ing; nev-er can wait 'til quit-ting time, just to

Countryfied - 2 - 1

Chorus:

get down to the wa-ter, and to wet my fish-ing line. Well, I'm coun-try-fied;

I like my chick-en fried. I like to walk bare-foot-ed through the coun-try-

side. Well, I'm coun-try folk; I like to roll my smokes.

I love to hear a fid-dle play-ing Cot-ton-eyed Joe.

Joe.

Verse 2:
Never been much on conversation,
They say I'm hell when I get tight;
Love to get out my old coon dog
And shine up a few at night.
I like to sit around my campfire
And hear old Blue at work,
Runnin' them cagey critters
For everything he's worth. *(To Chorus:)*

Verse 3:
I like to sit down with my woman,
Watch T.V. after supper time;
Snuggle real close together,
'Cause she knows how to ease my mind.
Talk about days when we were younger,
Think about days when we get old;
Like the lazy days of summer,
We like to watch the fallin' snow. *(To Chorus:)*

Countryfied - 2 - 2

MOUNTAIN DEW
(Good Old Mountain Dew)

Words and Music by
SCOTT WISEMAN and
BASCOMB LAMAR LUNSFORD

Bright moderato

Verses

1. Not __ very far from me, there's an old hol - low tree where you
2. preach - er came by, with his head h'ist - ed high, said his
4. my un - cle Mort, he's sawed off and short, and he
3. *(Instr. solo ad lib)*

lay down a dol - lar or two; __ then you go a - round the bend, then you
wife had took down with the flu; __ and he thought that we ought just to
meas-ures 'bout four foot two; __ but he thinks he's a giant, when you

Mountain Dew - 2 - 1

come back a - gain with a jug of that good old moun - tain dew._____
give her a snort of that good old moun - tain dew._____
give him a pint of that good old moun - tain dew._____

Chorus:

Oh they call it that old moun - tain dew,_____ and them that re - fuse it are

few,_____ oh I'll hush up my mug if you'll fill up my jug with that

good old moun - tain dew._____ 2. Now the
3.(Instr.)
4. Now ____ dew._____

Mountain Dew - 2 - 2

GUITAR MAN

Words and Music by
JERRY REED

1. Well, I quit my job down at the car wash; I left my ma-ma a good-bye
2.4. (see additional lyrics)
3. (Instr. solo ad lib) 5.6. etc. (Instr./vocal ad lib)

note; by sun-down I'd left Kings-ton with my gui-tar un-der my coat.

— I hitch-hiked all the way down to Mem - phis; got a room at the

Guitar Man - 4 - 1

man. *(Spoken:) We don't need a guitar man, son.*   So I   slept in the ho-bo

jun - gles;   I roamed a   thou - sand miles of   track,   'til I

found my - self in Mo - bile, Al - a - bam-a, in a   club they call "Big

Jack's."   A lit - tle   four piece band was jam - min', so I took my

Guitar Man - 4 - 3

guitar, and I sat in. I showed 'em what a band would

sound like with a swing-in' lit-tle gui-tar man. *(Spoken:) Show 'em son.*

D.S.

Verse 2:
Well, I nearly 'bout starved to death down in Memphis;
I run out of money and luck;
So I bummed me a ride down to Macon, Georgia
On a overloaded poultry truck.
I thumbed on down to Panama City;
Started checking out some of them all night bars;
Hoping I could make myself a dollar
Making music on my guitar.
I got the same old story at them all night piers;
There ain't no room around here for a guitar man.
(To 2nd ending)

Verse 4:
If you ever take a trip down to the ocean;
Find yourself down around Mobile,
Make it on out to a club called "Jack's",
If you got a little time to kill.
Just follow that crowd of people;
You'll wind up out on his dance floor,
Diggin' the finest little five piece group
Up and down the Gulf of Mexico;
And guess who's leading that five piece band?
Wouldn't you know it's that swinging little guitar man.

LOVE IN THE FIRST DEGREE

Words and Music by
JIM HURT and TIM DUBOIS

1. I once thought of love— as a pris-on, a
2. (see additional lyrics)

place I did-n't want to be;___ so long a-go___ I

made a de-ci-sion to be foot-loose and fan-cy free;___ but

Love In The First Degree - 3 - 1

Verse 2:
I thought it would be so simple,
Like a thousand times before;
I'd take what I wanted, and just walk away,
But I never made it to the door.
Now babe, I'm not begging for mercy;
Go ahead and throw the book at me.
If loving you is a crime, I know that I'm
As guilty as a man can be.
(To Chorus:)